A Fresh Approach
to Sight-Reading

Joining the Dots
for Violin

Grade 3

Alan Bullard

Violin Consultant: Douglas Blew

ABRSM

To the Teacher

Joining the Dots offers lots of material to help build skill and confidence in sight-reading. Used as part of regular lessons and practice, it will help pupils learn to read new music more quickly and easily, developing their awareness of fingerboard geography, their sense of key and other general musicianship skills.

The five books in the series cover the keys found in ABRSM's sight-reading tests at each of Grades 1–5, with a section for each key. Each section begins with warm-up and technical material ('Key Features' and/or 'Workouts'), followed by opportunities for improvisation ('Make Music') and several short pieces to sight-read ('Read and Play').

Key Features are a supplement to scales and arpeggios, and are provided here for those keys not found in the books for Grades 1 and 2. They can be played at various speeds and dynamics, and with the different bowing suggested, to help pupils to establish the 'feel' of each new key under the fingers.

Workouts are for warming up and exercising in the key. They are designed to be practised, and therefore explore slightly more advanced techniques than those found in sight-reading at this level. The first of each pair is the same throughout (transposed for each key), to help reinforce key familiarity, while the second is always different.

Make Music provides an opportunity for your pupils to build confidence in (and through) creative and imaginative work, and to develop aural skills. The activities here will also help to familiarize pupils with the 'feel' of the key, but using an approach that is not primarily notation-based. Activities include creating melodies using 'call and response' and by continuing a given opening. You and your pupils can approach these together in whatever way is most comfortable: for most pupils this will involve exploring the violin with some trial and error – experimenting is a good way to learn here!

Read and Play is the goal of each section – a number of short, characterful pieces, to be played at sight or after a short practice time, with the focus on keeping going. These lead up to and include the technical standard to be found in Grade 3 sight-reading and are a useful source of sight-reading material for those preparing for exams. The last piece in this section is sometimes slightly longer and more challenging than the pieces found in Grade 3 sight-reading. In all cases, the suggested bowing is a recommendation only.

Because the material is arranged to be at an equivalent level in each key, your pupils can 'jump in' to any section, using it alongside pieces, scales or arpeggios that are being learnt in that key. However, within each section it is recommended that pupils learn and play the Key Features (where provided) and Workouts before moving on to the Make Music and Read and Play material. No fingering is given, but it is suggested that you encourage the use of the 4th finger where appropriate.

Towards the end of the book you will find **More Pieces to Play**, including solo pieces, and duets and a trio suitable for group work. Some of these are longer and slightly more challenging than the pieces found in Grade 3 sight-reading. The material in this section can be used in any way you wish – as additional sight-reading practice or as pieces to learn quickly and play through for fun.

First published in 2013 by ABRSM (Publishing) Ltd, a wholly owned subsidiary of ABRSM,
24 Portland Place, London W1B 1LU, United Kingdom

Reprinted in 2016

© 2013 by The Associated Board of the Royal Schools of Music

AB 3710

Illustrations by Willie Ryan, www.illustrationweb.com/willieryan
Book design and cover by www.adamhaystudio.com
Music and text origination by Julia Bovee
Printed in England by Caligraving Ltd, Thetford, Norfolk,
On materials from sustainable sources

Dear Violinist,

Joining the Dots will help you to learn new music more quickly and easily.

In this book you will find a section for each key that you are likely to use in Grade 3 sight-reading.

In each section there are several different things to do:

Key Features to get you used to playing in the new keys

Make Music in which you can develop and explore musical ideas

Workouts to exercise your fingers and bowing arm

Read and Play where there are a number of short pieces to play – read the title, work out the rhythm, find the notes and, when you're ready, play the piece right through without stopping!

Towards the end of the book you'll find **More Pieces to Play**, including some longer pieces, and duets and a trio to play with your friends.

Enjoy Joining the Dots!

Alan Bullard

C major

Key Features

- Practise these at various speeds and dynamics, and with different bowing
- Always listen to the tuning

- Play this with separate bows throughout, or with one bow for each crotchet beat in bars 1–4

- Play this with separate bows throughout, or with one bow for each bar

Workouts

- Practise these workouts to warm up in the key of C major

- Keep a steady pulse, whether you play with straight or swing quavers

- Focus on smooth bowing and graded dynamics

Make Music

Morning Fanfare

- Make a tune in the key of C major by filling in the gaps in the music below
- Your teacher, or another pupil, plays the notated music, then you invent your own response of an equal length, perhaps using the lower two strings for contrast
- Count in two bars together to set the pulse
- Always keep going, in time, and finish on the note C
- Don't look at the music or at the other player's fingers – just listen

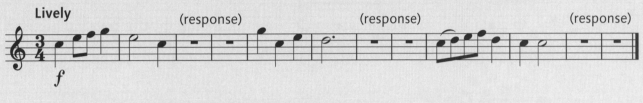

Marching

- Make up a tune in the key of C major, starting as shown
- Aim for a length of eight bars
- Finish on the note C

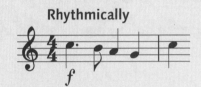

Read and Play

- Look at the time signature, then count two bars of crotchets and try out the rhythm
- Check the key signature and the first note, and get your fingers and bow ready
- If you like, try out the piece first, then play it right through without stopping!

Carefree

- Aim for a happy and bouncy character

C major

- Remember to try out the rhythm first, then check the key signature and the first note

In the Lift

- Imagine a lift steadily going up and down

Seriously Solemn

- Create a solemn mood by playing slowly but with a regular pulse

Dialogue

- Here's a piece to play with a friend
- The second player plays the same music, beginning when the first player reaches the asterisk sign (✳)

A minor

Key Features

- Practise these at various speeds and dynamics, and with different bowing
- Always listen to the tuning

- Play this with separate bows throughout, or with one bow for each crotchet beat in bars 1–4

- Play this with separate bows throughout, or with one bow for each bar

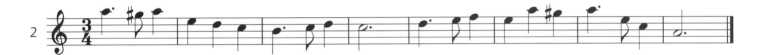

Workouts

- Practise these workouts to warm up in the key of A minor

- Keep a steady pulse, whether you play with straight or swing quavers

- Aim for a bright and lively feel and count the rhythm carefully, including the rests!

A minor

Make Music

Unhappy Conversation

- Make a tune in the key of A minor by filling in the gaps in the music below
- Your teacher, or another pupil, plays the notated music, then you invent your own response of an equal length, perhaps using the upper two strings for contrast
- Count in two bars together to set the pulse
- Always keep going, in time, and finish on the note A
- Don't look at the music or at the other player's fingers – just listen

Cheerful Tune

- Make up a tune in the key of A minor, starting as shown
- Aim for a length of eight bars
- Finish on the note A

Read and Play

- Look at the time signature, then count two bars of crotchets and try out the rhythm
- Check the key signature and the first note, and get your fingers and bow ready
- If you like, try out the piece first, then play it right through without stopping!

Musical Box

- Play lightly, to suggest the delicate old-fashioned charm of a mechanical musical box

• Remember to try out the rhythm first, then check the key signature and the first note

Journey Under Ground

• Take care to distinguish between the crotchets and the dotted crotchets

Russian Dance

• Play this colourful dance with precise rhythm

Story from the Past

• Here's a piece to play with a friend
• The second player plays the same music, beginning when the first player reaches the asterisk sign (✱)

G major

Workouts

- Practise these workouts to warm up in the key of G major

- Keep a steady pulse, whether you play with straight or swing quavers

- Aim for a sense of flow and poise

Make Music

The Sun Sets

- Make up a tune in the key of G major, starting as shown
- Aim for a length of eight bars
- Finish on the note G

Read and Play

- Look at the time signature, then count two bars of crotchets and try out the rhythm
- Check the key signature and the first note, and get your fingers and bow ready
- If you like, try out the piece first, then play it right through without stopping!

Miniature Minuet

- Aim to create the mood of a courtly dance of times past

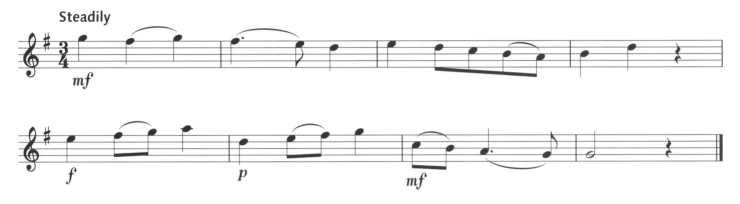

Taking Flight

- Play this lightly and energetically

Floating Away

- Here's a piece to play with a friend
- The second player plays the same music, beginning when the first player reaches the asterisk sign (✱)

E minor

Workouts

• Practise these workouts to warm up in the key of E minor

• Keep a steady pulse, whether you play with straight or swing quavers

• Grade the dynamics carefully here

Make Music

Always Cheerful

• Make up a tune in the key of E minor, starting as shown
• Aim for a length of eight bars
• Finish on the note E

With life

Read and Play

- Look at the time signature, then count two bars of crotchets and try out the rhythm
- Check the key signature and the first note, and get your fingers and bow ready
- If you like, try out the piece first, then play it right through without stopping!

Band in the Park

- Count the tied note carefully in this rhythmic march

Song of the Hills

- Aim for a spacious feeling by playing this with a rich tone

Austrian Dance

- Here's a piece to play with a friend
- The second player plays the same music, beginning when the first player reaches the asterisk sign (✱)

F major

Key Features

- Practise these at various speeds and dynamics, and with different bowing
- Always listen to the tuning

- Play this with separate bows throughout, or with one bow for each crotchet beat in bars 1–4

- Play this with separate bows throughout, or with one bow for each bar

Workouts

- Practise these workouts to warm up in the key of F major

- Keep a steady pulse, whether you play with straight or swing quavers

- Play this lightly and delicately

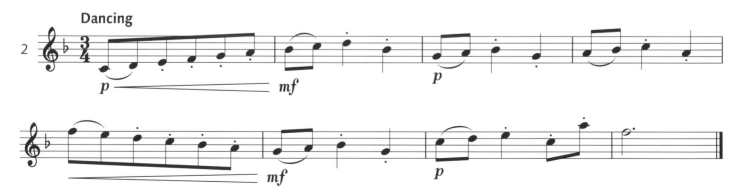

Make Music

Keeping Warm!

- Make a tune in the key of F major by filling in the gaps in the music below
- Your teacher, or another pupil, plays the notated music, then you invent your own response of an equal length, perhaps using the upper two strings for contrast
- Count in two bars together to set the pulse
- Always keep going, in time, and finish on the note F
- Don't look at the music or at the other player's fingers – just listen

May Morning

- Make up a tune in the key of F major, starting as shown
- Aim for a length of eight bars
- Finish on the note F

Read and Play

- Look at the time signature, then count two bars of crotchets and try out the rhythm
- Check the key signature and the first note, and get your fingers and bow ready
- If you like, try out the piece first, then play it right through without stopping!

Funfair

- Create the mood of a fairground with lively and rhythmic playing

F major

• Remember to try out the rhythm first, then check the key signature and the first note

Spring Song

• Observe the dynamics carefully

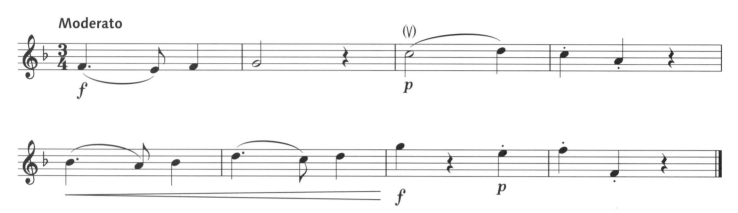

Toodle-oodle-oo

• In the last two bars, imagine you are tiptoeing out of the door

Footsteps

• Here's a piece to play with a friend
• The second player plays the same music, beginning when the first player reaches the asterisk sign (✱)

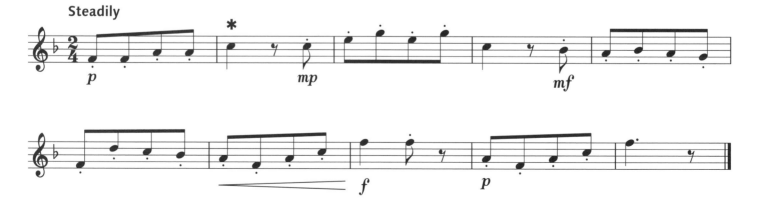

Key Features

- Practise these at various speeds and dynamics, and with different bowing
- Always listen to the tuning

- Play this with separate bows throughout, or with one bow for each crotchet beat in bars 1–4

- Play this with separate bows throughout, or with one bow for each bar

Workouts

- Practise these workouts to warm up in the key of D minor

- Keep a steady pulse, whether you play with straight or swing quavers

- Aim for a colourful tone

D minor

Make Music

Cloudy Sky

- Make a tune in the key of D minor by filling in the gaps in the music below
- Your teacher, or another pupil, plays the notated music, then you invent your own response of an equal length, perhaps using the lower two strings for contrast
- Count in two bars together to set the pulse
- Always keep going, in time, and finish on the note D
- Don't look at the music or at the other player's fingers – just listen

Woodland Path

- Make up a tune in the key of D minor, starting as shown
- Aim for a length of eight bars
- Finish on the note D

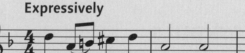

Read and Play

- Look at the time signature, then count two bars of crotchets and try out the rhythm
- Check the key signature and the first note, and get your fingers and bow ready
- If you like, try out the piece first, then play it right through without stopping!

Daybreak

- Play this with confident rhythm

• Remember to try out the rhythm first, then check the key signature and the first note

Journey's End

• Aim for a mood of expressive sadness, and keep the semiquavers light

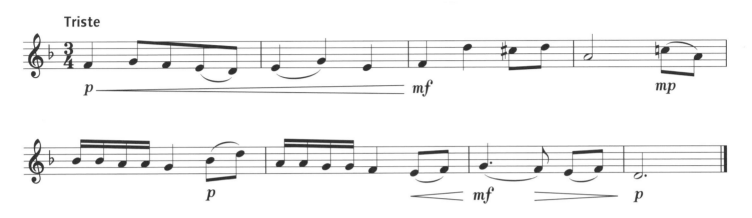

Striding Out

• Play the dotted rhythms tightly to suggest energetic exercise!

Hills and Valleys

• Here's a piece to play with a friend
• The second player plays the same music, beginning when the first player reaches the asterisk sign (✱)

D major

Workouts

- Practise these workouts to warm up in the key of D major

- Keep a steady pulse, whether you play with straight or swing quavers

Allegretto ritmico (quavers may be swung ♩♩ = ♩♪)

1

- Aim for a bright and clear sound, taking care over bow distribution

Alla marcia

2

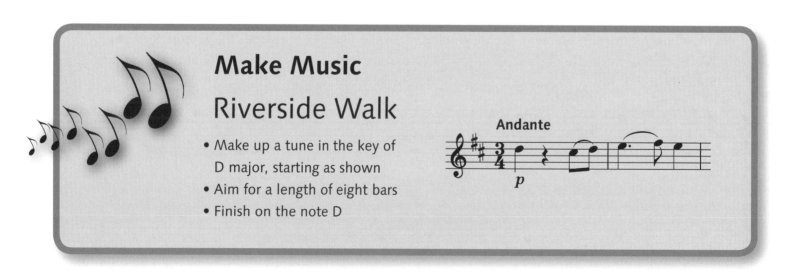

Make Music

Riverside Walk

- Make up a tune in the key of D major, starting as shown
- Aim for a length of eight bars
- Finish on the note D

Andante

Read and Play

- Look at the time signature, then count two bars of crotchets and try out the rhythm
- Check the key signature and the first note, and get your fingers and bow ready
- If you like, try out the piece first, then play it right through without stopping!

Ronnie's Ragtime Band

- Give this a sense of fun by playing with confident rhythm

Meditation

- Play this with a sense of calm and peacefulness

Echoes of Spring

- Here's a piece to play with a friend
- The second player plays the same music, beginning when the first player reaches the asterisk sign (✱)

Bb major

Key Features

- Practise these at various speeds and dynamics, and with different bowing
- Always listen to the tuning

- Play this with separate bows throughout, or with one bow for each crotchet beat in bars 1–4

- Play this with separate bows throughout, or with one bow for each bar

Workouts

- Practise these workouts to warm up in the key of Bb major

- Keep a steady pulse, whether you play with straight or swing quavers

- Aim for a lively and light feeling

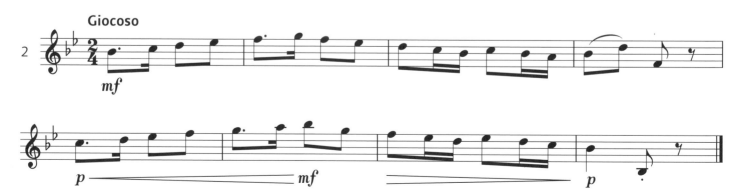

Make Music

Drifting Along

- Make a tune in the key of Bb major by filling in the gaps in the music below
- Your teacher, or another pupil, plays the notated music, then you invent your own response of an equal length, perhaps using the lower two strings for contrast
- Count in two bars together to set the pulse
- Always keep going, in time, and finish on the note Bb
- Don't look at the music or at the other player's fingers – just listen

Sound the Alarm!

- Make up a tune in the key of Bb major, starting as shown
- Aim for a length of eight bars
- Finish on the note Bb

Read and Play

- Look at the time signature, then count two bars of crotchets and try out the rhythm
- Check the key signature and the first note, and get your fingers and bow ready
- If you like, try out the piece first, then play it right through without stopping!

Dainty Dance

- Listen carefully to the tuning

Bb major

- Remember to try out the rhythm first, then check the key signature and the first note

Fanfare

- Play this with energy and a confident sound

Green Meadows

- Use plenty of bow to create a rich and expressive sound

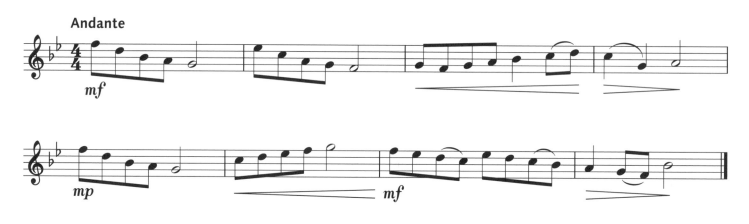

Canal Boat

- Here's a piece to play with a friend
- The second player plays the same music, beginning when the first player reaches the asterisk sign (✱)

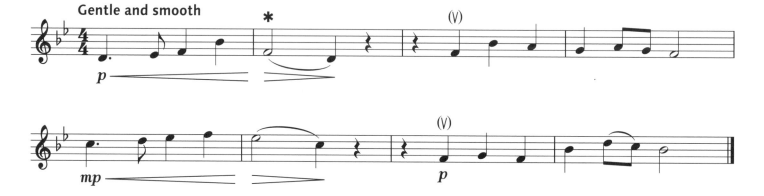

G minor

Key Features

- Practise these at various speeds and dynamics, and with different bowing
- Always listen to the tuning

- Play this with separate bows throughout, or with one bow for each crotchet beat in bars 1–4

- Play this with separate bows throughout, or with one bow for each bar

Workouts

- Practise these workouts to warm up in the key of G minor

- Keep a steady pulse, whether you play with straight or swing quavers

- Distinguish carefully between the different finger patterns

G minor

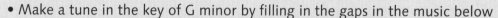

Make Music

Falling Rain

- Make a tune in the key of G minor by filling in the gaps in the music below
- Your teacher, or another pupil, plays the notated music, then you invent your own response of an equal length, perhaps using the lower two strings for contrast
- Count in two bars together to set the pulse
- Always keep going, in time, and finish on the note G
- Don't look at the music or at the other player's fingers – just listen

Climbing High

- Make up a tune in the key of G minor, starting as shown
- Aim for a length of eight bars
- Finish on the note G

Read and Play

- Look at the time signature, then count two bars of crotchets and try out the rhythm
- Check the key signature and the first note, and get your fingers and bow ready
- If you like, try out the piece first, then play it right through without stopping!

Who's at the Door?

- Imagine an insistent tapping on an old wooden door

- Remember to try out the rhythm first, then check the key signature and the first note

The Lonely Goldfish

- Distinguish carefully between the quavers and the dotted quavers

Mr Mystery

- Take care over the dynamic contrasts here

Distant Memories

- Here's a piece to play with a friend
- The second player plays the same music, beginning when the first player reaches the asterisk sign (✱)

A major

Workouts

- Practise these workouts to warm up in the key of A major

- Keep a steady pulse, whether you play with straight or swing quavers

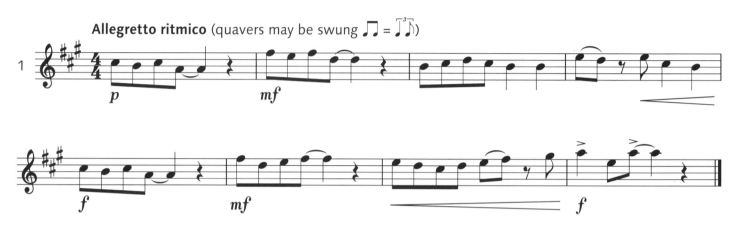

- Aim for clear contrasts between the phrases

Make Music

A Sunny Day

- Make up a tune in the key of A major, starting as shown
- Aim for a length of eight bars
- Finish on the note A

Read and Play

- Look at the time signature, then count two bars of crotchets and try out the rhythm
- Check the key signature and the first note, and get your fingers and bow ready
- If you like, try out the piece first, then play it right through without stopping!

The Bee

- Aim for a mood of gentle buzzing!

Climbing the Hill

- Notice how the music gets louder as you climb to the top

Characterful Conversation

- Here's a piece to play with a friend
- The second player plays the same music, beginning when the first player reaches the asterisk sign (✱)

More Pieces to Play

- On the remaining pages you will find a variety of solo pieces of different lengths, and some duets and a trio to play with your friends
- You can use these for playing at sight, or as pieces to learn on your own or with your teacher
- Before you start to play, don't forget to check the key signature and time signature, make sure you are happy with the rhythm, and then get your fingers and bow ready

Snowy Mountains

Crossing the Stream

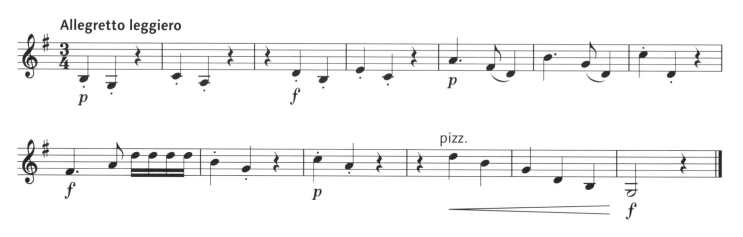

In Romantic Mood

Spreading Branches

Caterpillar Tracks

The Wizard

Neat Feet

Sunbeams

Whirlpool

Empty Landscape

Ready for a Rest!

Holiday Time

More Pieces to Play

Interrupted March

Longing

Dance Steps

Waterside

More Pieces to Play

Washing-Up Rag